Fix the

By Liza Charlesworth

T0298072

ISBN: 978-1-339-02677-0

Art Director: Tannaz Fassihi; Designer: Tanya Chernyak
Photos ©: pp1, 5: Rawpixel.com/Shutterstock.com. All other photos © Getty Images.
Copyright © Liza Charlesworth. All rights reserved. Published by Scholastic Inc.

3 4 5 6 7 8 9 10   68   32 31 30 29 28 27 26 25 24

Printed in Jiaxing, China. First printing, August 2023.

SCHOLASTIC

A kid spills milk.

A kid drops stuff.

Can kids make a mess?
Yes, yes, yes!

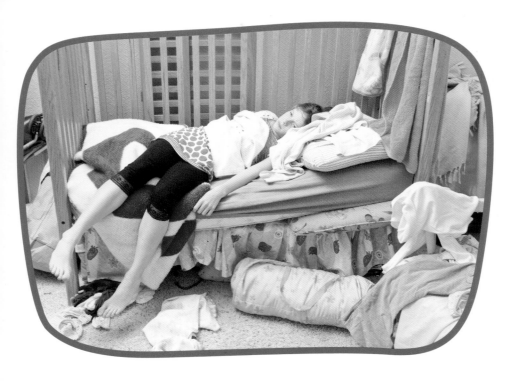

A mess can be bad.
But do not yell and fuss.

Do not huff and puff.
Get up and fix the mess.

Fill it up!

Mop it up!

Dust it off!

Toss it in a can!

You will see a lot less mess,
if you get up and fix it!